"It Will Do No Harm to Try It"

The Home Remedies Diary of Elias Slagle, 1859

Edited by Jim Long

Published by:
Long Creek Herbs
P.O. Box 127
Blue Eye, MO 65611
www.Longcreekherbs.com

With grateful recognition to the Bushwhacker Museum and
the Vernon County Historical Society, Nevada, Missouri, for allowing
the use of the contents of Mr. Slagle's diary.

ISBN #1-889791-14-8

Copyright©2003, Jim Long
Long Creek Herbs
P.O. Box 127
Blue Eye, MO 65611
www.Longcreekherbs.com

Elias Slagle's

Book

January 3th 1851

Elias Slagle, age 83, taken in Houston, Texas in 1916
Photo courtesy of Bushwhacker Museum, Nevada, Missouri

Preface

I first read about Elias Slagle's diary of folk remedies when a friend sent me a clipping out of the Nevada, Missouri *Daily Mail*. The article, written by Patrick Brophy, detailed some of the "cures" recorded, as well as giving some information about how the Bushwhacker Museum, where Brophy was curator, had come to be in possession of the diary.

I contacted Mr. Brophy and thus began my research into Elias Slagle. Brophy let me see and copy material from the diary and I was immediately intrigued by the text.

Over time I have studied the writing, both for clarity and for clues to information about the man who wrote it. The entire collection appears to be taken, verbatim, from a variety of sources. The remedies give clues to their origin as well as clues to the fears and prejudices of the culture of the mid-1800s.

We know very little of Elias Slagle's life except that as a young man he began collecting the remedies from healers he encountered on his travels. His record of remedies is dated with the beginning date of January 3, 1859. Some of the entries likely come from patent medicine flyers, broadsides, almanacs and newspaper stories. Others are obvious, by spelling and wording, to have been recorded verbatim as someone spoke.

Mr. Slagle wasn't a doctor, even by the standards of the mid-1800s. He may have wanted to be a physician, but more likely he simply wanted medical information as he looked toward taking on the responsibilities of having a family. It was common in those days to put together materials for life on the frontier, assembling it before heading West.

His diary was begun when he was 18 years old, and he married six years later. It is entirely likely, even probable, that his beginning this diary was just part of a larger preparation he made for life on the Frontier.

I

He was living in his birthplace, Bucycrus, Ohio, when the diary was begun. He became by trade a model and pattern maker, creating the specific patterns and models from which machine parts were made, expanding upon that trade while serving in the Navy during the Civil War. After working in that same capacity for the city of Newbern, North Carolina after the War, he moved to Texas then later Kansas, where he pursued the pattern and model making business for many years.

Unable to find surviving family members to add information to the text and seeking any additional, even remote enlightenment into who Mr. Slagle was, (and out of pure, simple curiosity) I consulted Martha Brown, a highly-regarded, Certified Graphologist, for her possible impressions of Mr. Slagle's temperament. Mrs. Brown has taught graphological analysis for many years and has worked as handwriting analyst for many major U.S. corporations. Her analysis of Slagle's handwriting follows and is included to give some tiny glimpse into the character of the author of this remedy diary. I had little information to offer Mrs. Brown at the time she performed her handwriting analysis. I didn't then know what his profession had been, but her intuitions served her well in her examination of Mr. Slagle's personality as seen in his penmanship.

The diary entries are given in this volume with virtually no editing, left with Slagle's spellings, punctuation and grammar. Explanations of the terms, plants and methods that follow each entry are from my own research and knowledge, and are meant to illustrate and enlighten Slagle's entries. The title, "It Will Do No Harm to Try It" comes from Slagle's own words in one of his recorded formulas.

I gratefully acknowledge the Bushwhacker Museum's kind permission to reproduce the material here. Mr. Brophy, of the museum, described the way the Museum came into possession of the material:

"The auctioneer of the Kenneth Young (a daughter and

son-in-law of Slagle) estate called me to say there were some interesting bits of information that likely would not sell at auction and I might be interested. I drove over to Richards, Missouri and loaded a bunch of junk in my car, much of it junk, indeed. The Slagle diary was the gem, as I discovered later. But for me the diary would have been burned."

A brief, written history of Slagle was recorded by Mrs. Salome Jane Slagle, his wife, with some of it seemingly recorded by Slagle himself, in his own words, or at least dictated by him. Spelling and punctuation are theirs:

Pasadena, Harris County, Texas, January 1st, 1906. A family record of Mr. Elias Slagle & his wife. To all whom this may concern:

I, E. Slagle has on the above date written out his family record. First: Mr. E. Slagle was born on the 10th day of October, 1833 in a little log house on the banks of the Sanduskey River (east) and near Bucyrus in Crawford Co & state of Ohio.

(An entry with his date of death was added later, possibly by one of his children): **Died October 22, 1917 at home, Passadena, Texas. Buried in Oakwood Cemetery, Bucyrus, Ohio.**

Second:

Mrs. S. J. *(Salome Jane)* **Slagle was born Nov. 13, 1841 in the city of Bucyrus in the County of Crawford & state of Ohio. An entry written in at this point says that she died 12:30 a.m. at Minnies, Richards, Vernon County, Missouri, July 30th, 1921. Buried in Oakwood Cemetery, Bucyrus, Ohio).**

Mr. E. Slagle was by occupation that of a model and pattern maker. Served 4 years in the U.S. Navy during the Civil War and also a year and a half as a pattern maker in the city of Newbern, N.C. in the U.S. Q.M.T. I am on pension roles at $12 per month. Was married to my present wife, Miss

S. J. Werst on the 29th day of August, 1865 at her parents home in the city of Bucyrus, Ohio. Worked at my trade in Bucyrus up to about 1880 and emigrated to Kansas and took up my trade in the machine work at Ft. Scott for some 14 years and moved to Texas and went out of business at my trade and took up that of farming.

January 1, 1906

Analysis of Mr. Slagle's Handwriting by Martha Brown

Impressions of Mr. Slagle by handwriting analyst (who did not have access to the above recorded information. At the time of the handwriting analysis this author had no idea as to what Mr. Slagle's occupation had been but note how his personality must have added to his exacting occupation of pattern maker):

"I wish to express my gratitude to Mr. Long and the Bushwhacker Museum of Nevada, Missouri for this unusual opportunity to explore this unique manuscript on herbal medicines by Mr. Elias Slagle.

Mr. Long asked if I could tell him about the lifestyle of Mr. Slagle from his unusual handwriting. The writing style in 1859 was quite different from our modern day script, but there are many clues to the inner man.

I believe an old fashioned ink pen, or possibly a quill pen, was used. The uneven flow of ink is apparent throughout this entire sample which must be evaluated in a different manner from modern day methods. The spelling is also of his era such as "cian" pepper for cayenne pepper. Also, "shugar" for sugar.

Elias Slagle was a future-oriented individual that was dedicated to his belief in herbs and their values for helping the world to be healthier. Strong pressure (of the pen) would be the key to his deep feelings. Enthusiasm is so strongly shown that I'm quite sure that herbs were his main topic of conversation.

Organizational ability shows through every page of his manuscript. However, I believe the original was written on lined paper which gave him guide lines on the way he would express himself. This (organizational skill) also indicates leadership qualities and his desire to help humanity.

Credit must be given this gentleman for perfectionism in his work. The attention to the most minute details in his writing gives credibility for his many cures. Exact is the right word!

Mr. Slagle was rigid in his thinking to the extreme of being stubborn. This speaks highly of his dedication to his work. He was quite capable of defending his views - but it was done in a diplomatic manner.

The unusual use of capital letters brings emphasis and strength to his thought processes. He wanted every one to completely understand what he was saying. Another unusual way of calling attention to his thinking process was the reversal of the slant of his writing as found in the word "kills" in the cure for cancer.

The symmetry shown in his script tells of the excellent balance that he had between the mental and the physical worlds. He was an earthy gentleman with a well-developed attitude for all life. Intuition could have been a strong helper, too.

This gentleman could analyze situations with great speed and reach a solution far ahead of the average individual. He seemed to be rushing to meet tomorrow.

There is some caution (in his penmanship) which adds to his perfectionism. I believe he was sure of every remark before placing it in the manuscript. His motto must have been "test" and "retest" along with the knowledge gleaned from other experts in the field.

In my opinion, Elias Slagle was a gentleman far ahead of his time. May he rest in peace for a life well spent."

Martha E. Brown, August 23, 1991

Cure for Bronchitis

Compromin mullen leaves Smoked in a new pipe, one in which tobaco has never been used, is a Sure and certain cure for bronchitis.

The remedy is simple and innocent, and is not the remedy of a retorted physician.

Feaver & ague
15 gr of quinine
15 gr of blue mass
12 gr of cian pepper (or capicon)
mix in 12 pills.

you take them after the feaver is off, 2 after the feaver is off 2 at noon 2 in the evening & soon til it is Stoped.

The
Cures

Recorded by Elias Slagle, beginning in 1859. Spellings and terms are entirely his and reproduced here as he wrote them with words corrected for clarity only when absolutely necessary. In some instances a word is unclear in the original text and in those instances I make a guess as to the word and you will find it (thus?) with a question mark. My explanations of the illness and of the plants or medicines used, follow each entry. You will notice that there are remedies for some of the same maladies in several places. Mr. Slagle evidently just made an entry every time he encountered a remedy without thought of organizing them into categories, although he added an index at a later date. The listings are not alphabetical nor organized in any manner except for when Mr. Slagle found the remedy and felt the need to record it.

The information in Mr. Slagle's diary tells us a great deal about life in the mid-1800s. First, we can tell that people were terrified by disease. Smallpox, diphtheria, malaria, fevers, poison snakes, rabid dogs and sick horses were a constant worry for people who left the comforts of their hometown and traveled West to make a new life for themselves.

We can learn from the text that all matter of home remedies were being written about in newspapers of the day, without regard to whether the remedy actually worked or not. We can tell that people believed disease was caused my mysterious "vapors" that rose up out of swamps and dark forests. We see that people believed they could drive off disease in the sickroom by burning incense or creating vapors by the burning of herbs or chemicals. We can see that people of Mr. Slagle's time believed that bathing often was a contributing cause of illness. Now we realize that the lack of hygiene contributed to many maladies such as body lice, scabies, infections and dysentery.

Although the entries in his diary are not extensive, they do hold many interesting clues as to what life was like when Elias Slagle began recording formulas in his diary in 1859.

Cure for Bronchitis

Common mullen leaves smoked in a new pipe, one in which tobaco has never been used, is a sure and certain cure for bronchitis. The remedy is simple and innocent and is not the remedy of a retired physician.

It's interesting that Slagle recorded this as "not the remedy of a retired physician." Bad physicians didn't stay in business very long. Thus, the remedy of a working doctor meant that the doctor was good enough not to have been driven out of business by patients who received bad treatment.

Mullein (*Verbascum thapsus*) is a biennial plant, not native to the U.S., but was well-established over the eastern and probably the central, portions of the U.S. by the early 1800s. Porcher (in *Resources of the Southern Fields & Forests*, 1863) records Mullein being used for a variety of things: "A decoction of the flowers and leaves as tea, is beneficial in dysentery and tenesmus...a large quantity of the flowers will even induce sleep, so active is the narcotic principle it contains." Many other sources list the leaves of this plant as effective for bronchitis. Foster (in *Peterson's Field Guide to Medicinal Plants*) lists it as an expectorant, demulcent, antispasmodic, diuretic, for chest colds, asthma, bronchitis, etc. He also gives warning that the leaves contain rotenone and coumarin.

Feaver & Ague

15 grams of quinine
15 grams of blue mass
12 grams of cian peper (or capsicum, Slagle's notation)
Mix in 12 pills
You take them after the feaver is off, 2 at noon, 2 in the evening and so on until it is stoped.

Quinine comes from the bark of the cinchona tree, a South American tropical species. Cinchona bark had been used by native peoples of the tropics for centuries for preventing and treating malaria. However, the first use of cinchona bark for malaria by Europeans is recorded by monks in 1633. Two French chemists then isolated the active alkaloid from cinchona bark in 1820. They named it "quinine" for an Inca term, quina-quina, meaning "bark of barks."

By 1823 the first quinine factory began operation in Philadelphia. Dr. John Sappington, in Arrow Rock, Missouri, was mixing and selling his own anti-fever pills in the 1830s (known as Sappington's Fever Pills) and he was a major distributor of quinine for settlers who were on the trail drives heading west on the Oregon and Santa Fe Trails. Quinine was the only effective treatment for malaria. Sappington is credited with making it possible for settlers to move westward with protection from malaria.

Blue Mass was also known as Mass of Mercury or Blue Pills. Some Materia Medica lists it under Massa Hydrargyri. Here are the ingredients, still in general use as late as 1927: Oleate of mercury, honey of rose, glycerin and althea. It was, in other words (due to the inclusion of mercury) a poison. Little was known in those days about the effects of mercury poisoning and it shows up in a variety of remedies.

Ague Cure
Take 1 oz. of madder in 1 qt. water, boil both together til you git the strength all out, Strain it off, then take 2 qt. cider mix both together then take 2 teaspoonfuls twice a day. (It is a sickning mixture).

The ague (pronounced "Aag-you") was a fever with periods of chilling, alternating with fever and sweating. Ague was a common name for malaria. Quinine was becoming available, but all kinds of remedies abounded for use when nothing else was at hand.

Madder was a common dye plant. In 1855 the U.S. Patent Office Report records that twenty million pounds of madder was imported for calico-printing, dyeing, and other uses, according to Porcher. Most likely the madder referred to in this remedy is either northern bedstraw *(Galium boreale)* or rough bedstraw *(Galium asprellum)*, both commonly called madder. Both plants are native to Ohio, Delaware, upward to Canada and south as far as Missouri.

Cure for Cancers

The process is this: A piece of sticking plaster is placed over the cancer, with a circular piece cut out of the centre a little larger than the cancer, so that the cancer and a small circular rim of healthy skin next to it were exposed. Then a plaster made of chloride of zinc, blood-root and wheat flour, is spread on a piece of muslin of the size of the circular opening, and applied to the cancer for twenty-four hours.

On removing it the cancer will be found to be burnt into, and appear the color and hardness of an old shoe sole, and the circular rim outside of it will appear white and par-boiled, as if scalded by hot steam. The wound is now clean, and the outside rim soon supprates and the cancer comes out a hard lump, and the place heals up.

The plaster kills the cancer so that it sloughs out like dead flesh, and never grows again. This remedy was discovered by Dr. Fell, of London, and has been used by him for six or eight years, with unfailing success, and not a case has been known of the reappearance of the cancer where this remedy has been used.

Cancers were any kind of skin problem that didn't go away. There once were all kinds of skin cancers, big ulcerous, ugly things that people suffered with and collectively called cancer. Anything, such as an infected boil might also be called a cancer. Surgery wasn't common for such things, so all kinds of topical treatments were used. Bloodroot *(Sanguinaria canadensis)* historically was used for externally for removing warts and internally for a variety of ailments. Pharmaceutical experiments have shown that the alkaloid sanguinarine, from bloodroot, has antiseptic, anesthetic and anticancer activities *(Peterson's Field Guide to Medicinal Plants)*. Zinc preparations are still used topically for treating many skin ailments including psoriasis.

How to make Itch Salv

Take 1 table spoon full (little heaping) of hogs fat, with out salt in it, 1 tea spoon ful (even) of red percipity, 2 tea spoons ful venic turpentine. Melt the lard mix in the red percipity - let it git cold then mix in the venic turpentine. Then it is fit for use. Rub twice a week and bathe (sparingly?) and don't you-git-wet.

"The Itch" was a common problem back in the days of straw and cornshuck mattresses and poor personal hygiene. Bed sheets were seldom washed, if used at all, and the itch mite *(Sarcoptes scabiei)* commonly infected bed clothes and thus, anyone who slept there. Scabies is the common name today for this problem. Once the parasite got under the skin, itching was constant and severe and people used all kinds of awful things to try to get rid of it. Stories abound of people who were driven nearly insane by the itch and would try baths in kerosene, turpentine, give themselves poison ivy or burn themselves with mercury to try to rid themselves of the problem. Percipity was likely a colloquial name for pokeroot *(Phytolacca americana)* as other references don't list that name. Pokeroot, boiled and mixed with lard was one of the more common treatments for scabies and has been used well into the twentieth century for that purpose.

"Venic turpentine" is imported Venice turpentine and was made from pine sap.

To Make Bitters

It consist in: 1 hand ful of ratil root
1 half pint burdock seed, 1 half pound Juniper Berrys
Take a good fat pitch pine knot, esafil(?) one handfull
2 quarts of good rum, or brandy the Ratil root & Burdock seed. You will bile in 1/2 gallon water down to one pint, the strength is very hard to get out. Then you mix all together and let stand. Corke up one week and then it is fit for use.

It is necessary to keep it corked all the time. You can make as much as you feel according to the ingredients you put in. You can add more or less Juniper Berrys after you have used some of the bitters.   S. Norton's Rx

Bitters were a common remedy for all kinds of stomach complaints and thousands of formulas existed. Doctors of the time regularly prescribed doses of bitters, and generally made the mixtures themselves. Later, after the Civil War, general stores and pharmacies sold ready-made bitters and lots of families had their own recipe for making bitters, as well. Some of these old recipes for bitters became the patent medicines of the late 1800s and many persisted until the establishment of the Food and Drug Administration made them illegal in the early 1900s.

Ratil root is most likely Rattleroot (*Cimicifuga racemosa*) also known as black cohosh or black snakeroot, a common ingredient in bitters and a plant that remains of some commercial value today. It was still listed in the directory of official plants in the 1927 edition of *Materia Medica*. In that reference it is listed as an alterative, diuretic, diaphoretic, expectorant, anti-spasmodic, sedative and as a cardiac stimulant often used in place of digitalis. So it would seem that bitters, made with this plant, did, indeed, have benefits if used properly.

Burdock root *(Arctium lappa)* is still used as a blood purifier today and is listed as a diuretic and for stimulating bile secretion, sweating, gout, liver and certain kidney ailments. Other ailments where burdock was traditionally used includes rheumatism; seeds used for sore throats, insect bites, and as an external wash for eczema and similar skin eruptions.

Cure for Teter Worm
Take red root - cut it in thin slices laying in good cider vinegar for 24 hours. Apply to worms.

"Teter"is a misspelling of tetter, a term applied to various skin diseases such as psoriasis and eczema and is characterized by eruptions and itching. People didn't know what the cause of tetter was and often it was believed that tiny tetter worms got under the skin, thus the entry at the end of the remedy to"Apply to worms."

Red root was another name for bloodroot *(Sanguinaria canadensis)*, commonly used for internal and external complaints. The 1927 *Materia Medica* lists bloodroot for tonic, emetic, stimulating expectorant, croup, asthma, jaundice, dyspepsia. *Peterson's Field Guide to Medicinal Plants* considers raw bloodroot to be toxic and gives a warning not to take it internally. Further, this source lists the root juice as being applied to warts; experimentally the juice has been shown to be antiseptic with anticancer activity. Bloodroot is used commercially today as a plaque-inhibiting agent in toothpaste, as well as being used in mouthwashes.

With that in mind, the bloodroot, combined with vinegar, would have worked as an antiseptic. Vinegar alone has been shown beneficial in treating skin ailments such as fungal infections and warts. These two materials, the herb and the vinegar, would likely have been an effective remedy for some types of tetter and skin and nail infections!

7

A Receipt for horsness

Take one drachm of horse radish fresh scraped; infuse it in four ounces of water, put it in a close vessel for two hours then make it in a (paste?) with an ounce of vinegar. Take a good teaspoon full at a time every morning & evening and every 2 hours.

Horseradish (*Armoracia rusticana*) is not native to the U.S., but followed settlement as people moved westward. Once planted in a garden spot, it usually remained long after the garden was abandoned. Roots were then, and are still, ground and used as a condiment. Tea of the roots were used medicinally as a diuretic and antiseptic; used for coughs, bronchitis, catarrah; poultices of the root used for rheumatism and congestion. Scientific evidence confirms horseradish's use as antibiotic, and it also has been shown to have some anti-tumor activity.

For Pimples on a Child

For pimples breaking on a child take tar and beef's tallow. Warm it so as to infuse together. Put it by for use. Grease the child all over mornings & evenings.

Can you imagine? Tar and feathers have been a punishment for indiscretions for centuries, and this isn't far from that. Most likely, some parents saw pimples as an indiscretion, something brought upon the teenager by bad behavior, bad habits, bad thoughts. The suffering from the treatment was more than likely seen as part of the cost for the cure.

Beef tallow, mixed with tar and slathered all over a child (presumedly only spreading it on the skin where there were pimples) would have been a sticky, ugly mess. But, oh, the humiliation of wearing tar as a remedy!

Many kinds of wood tars were used for medicine, both internally (in the form of elixirs, tar waters, tinctures) and externally.

Besides tar from pine, beechwood, birch, aspen and juniper were recognized as official medications by pharmacopeias until well into the twentieth century.

According to medical texts there was benefit to be had from the application of tar, although caution was given that tar shouldn't be applied directly to the face (thus the addition of the beef tallow) as it would cause staining. Grandpa's brand Pine Tar Soap has been manufactured since the late 1800s and is still available and useful for both dry and oily skin as well as pimples, eczema and other skin conditions.

Of course, imagine the poor teenager of that time, slathered all over with tar and lard. Try and imagine going to school looking like that. This remedy certainly did nothing to encourage school attendance.

A Cleasning & Healing Salve

Take inside bark of Boartree, Shumak root & Bitter Sweet root of the 2 former an equal quantity of the latter as much as the two together, fry them in hogs lard or fat. Put by for use.

Boartree isn't listed elsewhere by that name, but the name may have been a colloquialism for oak tree. Hogs were regularly grazed on acorns in the fall so calling the tree from which the acorns fell, a boar's tree would be logical.

Sumac root *(Rhus spp.)* and root of bittersweet (*Celastrus scandens)* are found in other folk remedy ingredient listings, bittersweet as being the more significant. Sumac shows up in various forms, the red, dried berries in the fall of the year being gathered for a lemonade-like beverage. The berries were used as medicines, mostly for flavoring as well as useful for the ascorbic acid they contained - which would help combat scurvy. Using the bark and the roots for medicine was less common. General healing salves were used for all kinds of skin ailments, rashes and first aid.

The use of the inside bark of an oak tree would add some tannin to the salve which would make this work like a drawing ointment, encouraging the skin to shrink together a bit and draw out infection or inflammation.

Bittersweet Root Salve
A good hand full of the bark of the root & 3/4 of a pint of hogs lard.

Several of Slagle's formulas include no directions. Either he believed he would remember the instructions, or they were understood. In this case, the root bark of bittersweet (*Celastrus scandens*) would have been cleaned of soil before being stripped from the root, then dried, broken up and pulverized in a mortar and pestle. The lard would have been warmed and the bark added, keeping the lard warm, but not hot, for several hours or longer. This was often done in an iron kettle, set on the hearth in the evening, so that the dwindling heat of the fire kept the lard warm.

The mixture would have been strained while warm, then poured into a container to cool. This was used like other salves for itching and skin irritations. Better salves had some beeswax or beef tallow added, to make the salve more solid. This particular salve, with only lard as a base, would become nearly liquid in summer and was probably stored in the cellar or tied onto a cord and hung part way down the well where it would stay cool in the same way that butter and milk was generally stored in those times.

Bite of a Snake
Take a table spoon full of Olive Oil inwardly & anoint the wound well with it.

Snake bite was a fearful thing in past centuries. Snakes were

10

mysterious, frightening creatures and the bite of a poisonous snake could be deadly. Little was known about which snakes were poisonous and which were not. The pioneer's general attitude of "subdue the wilderness" applied especially to snakes and every one encountered was killed out of fear and ignorance. All kinds of remedies abounded, none being an actual cure. The above was possibly effective in easing the fear for someone who had been bitten. If the snake was a non-poisonous variety, the cure might be given the credit, rather than the snake's lack of venom.

However, one item of interest about this remedy and the one following, is the use of olive oil. There were no olives growing in America so olive oil was imported. There was an attitude that things imported from more civilized countries, had more efficacy. The use of olive oil by itself attests to the high regard some people had for that mysterious, ancient oil. And the fact that it was both to be drunk as well as applied to the wound, speaks to the high regard in which this imported oil was held.

A most certain Remedy for a pain
Take Olive Oil & rub the part affected.

American Indians used willow tea, a forerunner of aspirin, for pain. Doctors carried opium derivatives for that purpose, but without either available, other remedies were sought. Possibly because olive oil was imported from a far away place, it was hoped it contained something to alleviate pain. Aside from the pleasantness of massage of the body part, the usefulness of rubbing on olive oil was negligible.

Cure for Croup
Take a table spoonful of pulverised allum & one (spoon?) of honey mix well. Then give a teaspoonful every 2 or 3 minutes till it operates any emetick (*emetic*) **which it will in a few minutes.**

Alum is manufactured from the minerals bauxite, cryolite, clay, alum-stone and alum-slate. Bauxite is aluminum hydroxide combined with iron, and rich deposits were being mined in Georgia and Alabama in the past. Alum was used medicinally, as well as being used in dyeing cloth, tanning, paper making and in home canning. It was a generally available material in Slagle's time.

Alumroot (*Heuchera americana*), also known as coralbells in our gardens today, was often used in place of manufactured alum, and has similar uses. It is considered styptic and astringent. Alum is the primary ingredient in styptic pencils, the lipstick-shaped tube of medicine applied to cuts on the face from shaving.

A tea of the leaves of alumroot was used for a sore throat gargle as well as for diarrhea, dysentery and piles. Roots were used on wounds and sores as a poultice. The action of alum and alumroot was to shrink the tissues of the skin.

As to its use for croup, it would have only had value in the tightening of the lining of the throat which might or might not have given any relief to the child suffering from the croup, depending upon the severity of the illness.

Cure for Consumption

Avoid spirituous liquors wholey. Wear flannel next the skin. Take every morning half pint new milk every morning mix the same with some expressed juice of hoarhound. It will give great ease and make the breathing powers strong and ease the pain entirely by 3 to 4 weeks.

Tuberculosis, or consumption, was a constant fear in the 1800s and was a tenacious killer of settlers. Epidemics wiped out entire families, even large portions of small towns and lots of theories abounded for the avoidance or cure for this disease. Virtually nothing was known about the disease when Slagle collected his remedies.

Some of the theories of where consumption came from included diet (too much salted beef), miasma (unseen vapors that rose up out of swamps and engulfed towns) and many others that seem ridiculous to us today.

Horehound *(Marrubium vulgare)* shows up in lots of remedies for illnesses involving the chest and throat. Experimentally horehound has shown to be an expectorant and to increase bile flow in the liver.

The spelling"hoarhound"still shows up in the middle of the twentieth century as seen in the tourist book, *Ozark Root Digger,* by Chick Allen, 1958. The plant is effective in helping reduce coughing and is the source of horehound cough drops which were commonly available throughout the late 1800s and through the middle of the 20th century.

Horehound is helpful in coughs and sore throats but would have had no value in treating consumption.

For Teter Worm
Red percipithic & fresh butter make an annointment.

Tetter is a term used for several kinds of skin ailments including eczema, itching and the like. It is entirely possible that people during this time of history believed that the condition was caused by a"Teter worm."

"Red percipithic" is likely to be another spelling for the "percipity"found elsewhere in Slagle's recordings. This was possibly pokeroot *(Phytolacca americana)*, but since the originator of this remedy designates it as"red" percipithic, it was more likely to refer to bloodroot *(Sanguinaria canadensis)*. Both were used in preparations like the one above.

A Cure for Feaver & Ague
1/2 oz. of cloves, 1/2 oz. cream tartar, 1 oz. Peruvian bark well pulverized. Put in a bottle of best port wine and take the

decoction on well days as fast as the stomach will receive it.

The reference to "well" days indicates that generally the person suffering from malaria (the ague) couldn't keep even liquids down part of the time. Another name for this illness was "intermittent fever" due to the fact that the disease would seem to leave, giving the patient "good days" only to reappear again. The disease was persistent, hanging on sometimes for months unless treated and generally resulting in death. In persistent cases the patient would have a so-called "well day" followed by days of being too sick to move, eat or drink. So the patient was to take this formula at the times that liquids could be kept down.

Peruvian bark *(Chinchonia)* was a respected treatment for malaria by the 1820s, and so this remedy would probably effect a recovery if the patient had access to Peruvian bark. However, the medical community at the time taught that Peruvian bark was a strong stimulant and should only be administered to ague patients *after* they had received strong emetics and purgatives, then were bled. This process lasted several days. Then, if the patient had survived the barbarism (many did not) they would be given a dose of Peruvian bark.

Imagine what the common treatment was: You contracted malaria and went to the doctor, so ill you had to be carried. His treatment included giving you herbs that made you vomit over and over, as well as a purgative, something that caused you to severely empty your bowels repeatedly for hours. After twenty four hours of this vomiting and purging, you were bled of a pint of blood and bandaged up with non-sterilized bandages. If, after another twenty four hours, you were still alive, you would be administered the decoction of cloves, cream of tartar and quinine - the very thing you should have been administered two days earlier! Many malaria patients did not survive the purging and bleeding stages of the treatment. Two French chemists isolated the essential part of Peruvian bark in 1820, calling it "quinine."

The drug's advantages were that exact amounts for treatment could be determined and no longer was it necessary to transport large amounts of the unprocessed root. By 1823 quinine was being manufactured in Philadelphia.

Dr. John Sappington, a doctor in Arrow Rock, Missouri began using quinine to treat malaria patients in the late 1820s. He demonstrated remarkable results with the drug, giving it at the onset of malaria and eliminating the use of purging and bleeding. In 1832 he began the wholesale manufacturing of what came to be called, "Sappington's Fever Pills." These were widely distributed by his own army of traveling salesmen who regularly visited the staging areas for wagon trains heading west on the Oregon and Santa Fe Trails. Doctors of the time dismissed him as a quack. In trying to change medical opinion and save lives, he wrote a book entitled, *Theory and Treatment of Fevers* in 1843. Each one of Sapppington's Anti-Fever Pills contained one grain of quinine, three-fourths of a grain of licorice and one-fourth grain of myrrh, with enough oil of sassafras for flavoring. He directed that one of these pills be given every two hours, "day and night, at any stage of the fever" until the disease was receding and thereafter the patient was to take occasional doses as long as the anemia and debility continued.

Doctors were slow to embrace this simple treatment, holding on to the purging and bleeding practice. In fact, at the beginning of the Civil War, in 1861, the U.S. Army's official directions for treating malaria still included bleeding and purging the patient, first, before administering quinine. Over time, though, Sappington's cures were so profound that the medical community came around to his methods. Little evidence of his influence shows up in medical histories, however.

In Slagle's remedy, cream of tartar and cloves were likely added for flavoring as the Peruvian bark was bitter. Quinine water, used by the British to treat and ward off malaria, evolved into the drink, gin and tonic, the lime being used to give some flavor (much like the cream of tartar may have done here) and the gin making the medicine more bearable.

Cure for Influenza

Take one ounce of Shugar Candy, 2 ounces Gum Arabic, 1/2 ounce liquorice. Let them be broken in a mortar then dissolved in one pint boiling water. When the mixture is cold add to it two tablespoonfulls of good Antimonial wine. Take 5 or 6 table spoon fulls in 2(?) hours and likon according to age.

Licorice *(Glycyrrhiza glabra)* has a long history for use as a digestive aid. Mixed with sugar, it would taste more pleasant.

Gum arabic is a gum exuded from an African tree, *(Acacia senegal)*. It was used as a thickener and stabilizer of candies, mucilage, pills and emulsions. It is still used today in herbal and pharmaceutical remedies.

The reference to antimonial wine would be wine in which antimony, a metallic element, in the form of a silver-white,crystalline material was added. It is used today in batteries, in the manufacture of flame-proofing compounds, paints and ceramic products. Antimonial wine was commonly kept on hand by doctors of the day. The directions were that the tartarated antimony was first added to hot water, cooled, then added to wine or sherry. It is listed as a diaphoretic, expectorant and emetic.

Cure for Indigestion Cholera

Morbus or minor complaints in children or any complaint in the stomach or bowels.

1/4 lb. crude or green or new Rhubarb, 1/2 oz. caraway seed, 1/2 oz Orange peel. Infuse them in one quart best fresh brandy & let it stand 12 hours before using. Dose for a groan person 2/3 of a wine or stem glass full for a day or every 6 hours if necessary. For a child a tea spoon full every 6 hours.

Morbus was a common term used for morbid, or serious. Rhubarb leaves are poisonous, but the stalks would be the parts used here. This most likely refers to the common garden rhubarb *(Rheum australe)* while the Chinese variety *(R. officinale)* was used as a medicinal herb, the roots being the part generally used.

The caraway seeds are used as a digestive and the orange peel was there for flavoring. It would likely have been an effective stomach stimulator.

It is interesting that this formula is similar to many recipes using rhubarb for jams, pies and marmalades. Orange peel, which was not readily available except as a dried herb and the caraway seed are both often combined with rhubarb, then boiled down with sugar to make a condiment.

Frozen Flesh

Mr. A Bronson of Meadville, Pa, says from fifteen years' experience, he finds that Indian meal poultice, covered with young hyson tea, softened with hot water, and laid over burns or frozen flesh, as hot as can be borne, will relieve the pain in five minutes.

The remedy here appears to have been copied from a broadside or newspaper. This was probably a useless cure, simply because putting on the Indian meal (cornmeal) poultice "as hot as can be borne" would likely do more harm than good. Serious burning would probably result if the poultice was applied that hot to flesh so numb and without feeling. Young hyson tea refers to a type of green Chinese tea whose young, tender leaves are curled or twisted, and is the first picking of tea and supposed to have more strength than tea picked on later harvests.

There was the belief that Indian meal, or corn meal as we

know it today, was beneficial as a drawing agent. Indeed, for the application on some kinds of wounds, it did act as a drawing agent, absorbing pus or fluids away from a wound.

However, applying it"as hot as could be borne"would certainly damage frostbite. In those days, slowly thawing the frozen flesh under cold water would have seemed counter-productive and many so-called cures only increased the injury.

Cure for Rattlesnake Bite

Take the yolk of an good egg and pit it in a teacup; stir in with it as much salt as will make it thick enough not to run off. Spread it as a plaster and apply it to the wound and we will insure your life for a sixpence.

I love this remedy! It not only shows how mysterious snakebite remedies were, how frightening such an injury was, but the lengths people would go to try to find a remedy.

It's just a guess, but the reference to "…and we will insure your life for a sixpence." probably dates this remedy as coming from much earlier when a sixpence was common currency. Sixpence was British currency, worth six pennies. The currency remained in circulation in the Colonies but would have probably not been common by the time Mr. Slagle was recording his cures.

There were, in actuality, no cures for rattlesnake bite. Either the person survived by pure strength (or a minimal dose of rattlesnake venom), or he died. The ones who survived would swear on a Bible that whatever remedy they used at the time had been effective. An egg and salt, applied to the wound would have been absolutely useless, no matter what insurances the doctor pronounced!

Ointment for the Cure of Piles

It is composed of 2 ounces of flour of sulphur, 1 ounce

of powdered nut galls, 1 grain of powdered opium, all intimately mixed with lard, until the ointment is of the proper consistency. It is applied to the parts affected twice every 24 hours until a cure results. This ointment has the appearance of being pretty good for the purpose designed.

Hemorrhoids, or piles, were even more common back in earlier times then they are now. Nut galls were from an insect that pestered the oak tree. The galls contained an insect egg, growing on the limb or leaf and were made of much the same material as the oak tree and contained large amounts of tannin. The tannin would help to shrink the hemorrhoids. Note the powdered opium, a commonly available pain killer until about 1912.

Note also the words, "intimately mixed." This simply refers to mixing the ingredients precisely and completely. Or it may have been a way of giving Slagle the recipe, but not sharing all of the methods. Good cooks and professional chefs use the same method today. When asked for one of their good recipes, they may give all of the ingredients except one, or they may omit the method that makes the recipe special. In this case, though, it appears that the term simply refers to mixing the ingredients thoroughly.

Cure for a Cold & Cough

Take sweet milk 1/2 tinful & 1 red pepper pad and put in with the sweet milk & let it steep & then drink as it (sours?)

Red pepper pad (pod), meaning cayenne pepper, in a cup of milk, letting it sit for awhile to allow the heat of the red pepper to disperse, was a common method of steeping some herbs. Sweet milk was a commonly understood designation, the opposite being either buttermilk or even soured milk. Without refrigeration milk would spoil quickly, although soured milk was used by cooks for making cottage cheese, cheese and other foods. This remedy stresses the use of fresh milk.

Cayenne pepper was somewhat new to American culture, particuilarly in the East. It came into general use around the 1830s and '40s due to the commerce that developed after the opening of the Santa Fe Trail. Mexicans and Indians in the Southwest had been using cayenne pepper for centuries for a variety of ailments. Frontiersmen had trouble swallowing hot peppers as their palates were not used to such heat, but because of the pepper's strength on the tongue, many uses were found for it in home remedies. Adding it to milk was a method of making it more palatable, in the same way that hot Mexican food often requires some sour cream, cheese or Mexican cream served on the side today.

The milk and cayenne pepper would have done little for a cold, but because it was exotic, much like the use of olive oil, it gave the patient some comfort and hope.

How to Make Pain Killer
One gallon of alcohol, one pound of gum Murr, 1 ounce of Cian pepper, 1 ounce of camphor.

"Gum Murr" refers to myrrh, a gum resin from India, Africa and Arabia and used in perfume and incense. Cian is cayenne pepper.

This is very similar to a pain rub and liniment used in the late 1800s and well into the 1960s, called Kloss's liniment. In that one, more ingredients were used, but the myrrh, alcohol and cayenne pepper were the basic ingredients. The liquid was used on mild burns, on sore gums, sore throats as a gargle, to treat rheumatism and other ailments.

Look how similar Slagle's formula is to the famous Kloss Liniment of the 1940s and revived in the back-to-the-land days of the 1960s:

    2 oz. gum myrrh
    1 oz. goldenseal
    1/2 oz. cayenne
    Dissolve in one quart alcohol and shake daily for ten days.

This formula is still sold in some health food stores and by pharmacists who formulate their own mixtures.

How to Make Spike Oil

Take seedar wood & split fine & fill a common cook pot & turn it upside down on a rock a little raise(d), then dab it all round below & leave a small place undobed. Then build a fire on the top of the pot & then the oil will run out. Then add spirits of turpentine enuff to thin it. (You run the Oil the same as you would tar).

This was a common method for making pine tar but in this instance cedar was used in place of pine. Cedar oil and cedar tar were commonly available as medicine until about the 1920s. The method described is simply a home method for heating the green wood while covered with a container and catching the sap as it is released.

The reference to "dab it all around" means that the pan, once inverted, would be sealed off from air with wet clay. The "small place undobed" meant that there was an opening left so that the tar could run out. The real trick to this method was to keep the tar from catching fire as it ran out from under the pot.

Spike oil in most instances refers to lavender spike oil but in this instance the term, "spike" refers to spikes of cedar wood.

Salve for Frost Bites

Wahls's? Frost Salve
24 ounces mutton tallow
24 ounces hog's lard, 4 ounces? of iron-red iron rust, 4

ounces Venice turpentine, 2 ounces oil of bergamot, 2 ounces bole Armenian, rubbed to a paste with olive oil. Heat together the tallow, lard and iron rust, in an iron vessel, stirring with an iron spoon constantly till the mass assume a perfectly black color; then add gradually the other ingredients stirring until well mixed. It is appied upon linen daily and its effect upon even the most painful, open frost sores is most extraordinary. In all probability for other similar wounds it would also be an excellent application.

Parts of this recipe are not legible, thus my addition of the question marks. The combination of mutton tallow and hog's lard would make for a softening salve as the lanolin from the sheep would be useful. Bergamot refers either to oil from *Citrus aurantium bergamia*, which is a small tree that bears sour, pear-shaped fruit, from which the aromatic oil comes that is used in perfumery and medicine (and the flavoring in Earl Grey tea). Or, it might refer to oil from any of several plants in the *Monarda* family, native to the U.S., used as tea and medicine and smelling somewhat like imported bergamot oil.

The addition of the red iron rust would add very little beyond coloring and when applied to frozen, probably discolored skin, might give the impression that the salve was helpful by its color. Armenian bole is a pale red earth used medicinally and in tooth powders.

Cure for Frozen Flesh

A piece of copperas dissolved in warm (lard or oil?), is a sure remedy for frozen hands & so forth. Soak the fingers or feet, or rub well on the nose or face.

Copperas is a greenish, crystalline, hydrated ferrous sulfate, used today in the manufacture of fertilizers, inks and in water purification. Many crystalline substances were used as medicine in the days when little was known about their chemical make up. The missing word is likely to be lard, or oil, as either were used as a carrier for such treatments.

A Salv to Draw

Take some brown sugar, say 1/2 & 2/3 soft soap or hard soap. Mix well. Spread on a rag & then apply to the affected part.

Notice the spelling of salve. Slagle seems to have kept the spelling of those whose remedies he recorded, even though he had spelled the word correctly in previous entries. One-half part brown sugar to two-thirds part soft soap could have been any amount desired, parts being spoons full or cups full. Soft soap is a soap made with olive oil while hard soap was made from lard or tallow.

Burnt Alum is good for proud flesh

Proud flesh refers to flesh that is sloughing off, such as around a wound or from frost bite. This simple entry with no other ingredients alludes to alum being used for a variety of ailments where contracting the vessels of the skin was useful. Burning the alum, or roasting it in advance, would have done little to help, but it made the formula seem more exotic than simply applying alum to the sloughing off area. Olive oil would have been a much better choice for treatment.

Sun Burn to Cure

Take 1 part lime, 1 part hog's lard & mix both together & spread it thin on the burns. The lime best be slacked.

Slacked lime means slaked lime, here referring probably to lime that has been pulverized to a very fine dust after being

23

heated, then mixed with a small amount of water. The hog's lard shows up many times in old treatments for burns, as does bacon grease and butter. None were effective for healing sunburn but did help to soothe the patient. The only useful part of this treatment was that it sealed off the burn from outside bacteria, keeping out infection. However, on mild burns, leaving the spot open to the air was more effective than covering it up.

Scarlet Fever

It is a strong tea made of dog fennel & be drank warm or cool frequently by the patient; a poultice of the leaves of the plant to be applied to the throat, and often renewed until relief is obtained. This plant is to be found in every part of the country, and we hope it will be given a thorough trial in all cases of scarlet fever. We heard of this remedy years ago, and were apprised that it will check the disease. We are again reminded of it, and give our leaders the benefit of a remedy which is stated to be efficacious in nearly all cases.

Dog fennel, also known as yarrow (*Achillea millefolium*) is a plant that is still sometimes used for colds, fevers, indigestion, gastric inflammations and internal bleeding. The plant also has strong blood-stopping properties and has been used in centuries past for that purpose as a battle wound herb. The botanical, Latin name for this plant, *Achillea*, alludes to the fact that this was an important medicinal plant on the battlefield, dating back to ancient Greek and Roman times. Named for Achilles, who died on the battlefield due to an arrow wound in his heel, when supposedly none of this plant was available to stop the bleeding.

Note here the reference to "our readers" which leads us to think the remedy appeared in an almanac or newspaper with Slagle copying it word for word. The remedy, however, would have had no beneficial effect on scarlet fever.

Cure for poison taken inwardly.
Take 2 gils of Sweet oil inwardly.

Sweet oil is olive oil and would work on some kinds of poison by coating the stomach, or by causing vomiting. A gill is 4 fluid ounces or 1/4 pint.

However, this certainly was not a remedy for all kinds of poisons. In a later century doctors knew that some poisons should be vomited up while other kinds should be treated in other ways. As a cure-all for poison, this remedy would have worked on some kinds of poisons and on others, not at all.

Worth Knowing

A young lady of this city, says the Philadelphia Post, while in the country some years ago, stepped on a rusty nail, run through her shoe and foot. The inflammation and pain were great and lockjaw was apprehended. A friend recommended the application of a beet taken fresh from the garden, and pounded fine, to the wound. It was done, and the effect was beneficial. Soon the inflammation began to subside, and by keeping on the crushed beet, changing it for a fresh one its virtue seemed to become insured, a speedy cure was effected.

This is obviously another item copied from a printed source.

Grated beet is a common wound treatment and does not mean literally grating up the beet, but rather means to cut it in half and roughen up the surface or mash. In my own family the tradition persisted into the 1960s that a beet, prepared that way and applied to a wound, would speed healing and draw out infection. In this formula, though, the beet was pounded.

Lockjaw, or tetanus, was a worrisome ailment as it was a miserable and frightening way to die. Stories persist in folklore about people starving to death from locked jaws from this disease and families of patients who had the disease would try just about any method for healing. A beet applied might have some benefit on a common boil or wound, but it would not prevent tetanus since that disease comes from bacteria in a wound.

Distemper in Doggs

Take sulphur & copperas in equal quantity of each; pulverize both & then stir them in sweet milk, to dissolve & to give this to the doggs. You give him some milk without anything in it, then pour but little of this mixture in the milk you give him at different times of the day say twice. You will take a heeping teaspoon full of sulphur & the same of copperas pulverized to one half pint sweet milk.

Sulphur was used for all sorts of ailments on animals as well as man. It did have some drawing properties. The powdered copperas would have done little for the animal, short of acting as a slow poison. If given in small doses, it would not have cured nor killed the animal. Both the sulphur and the copperas were bitter and would not likely have been swallowed by the dog.

Certain Cure for Asthma

This is said to be a certain cure for that distressing complaint, the asthma. In any quantity, say a quart of apple brandy, put as much common salt as will dissolve. When this is done it is ready for use. Take three table spoons full per day, one just before each meal. Several sufferers by this disease have been effectually cured by this recipe.

Nothing in this remedy appears to be helpful, but the patient would have gained some hope by the application of anything that resembled a treatment by possibly instilling a positive attitude. The one thing that would happen with this remedy is when the patient took the salty apple brandy, it would probably cause him to gag or choke, due to the salt. It's a bit like the remedies for asthma that include smoking a bit of mullein or other plant as it caused the patient to choke and cough, which was believed to help expel the ailment.

Colic in Horses

It is simply to pour cold water on the back of the animal for fifteen or twenty mintes. Pour the water on from the withers to the loins, so as to run profusely over the sides and stomach. It will give almost entire relief in one hour.

There were old timers who swore by this remedy and I remember hearing my grandfather describe this in the 1950s as a method he had used. Colic was a dreaded disease in horses. Remember, having a horse become ill was like having your only car up on blocks and unavailable to use. Little was known about animal health and access to veterinarians was rare. Sometimes the horse got better, sometimes not. If the former, then the farmer credited the remedy.

To Purify the atmosphere when a sick room

Saucers full of chloride of lime moistened with a few drops of vinegar and water will purify the atmosphere of a sick-room in a few minutes.

Lime and vinegar combined let off vapor which was believed beneficial. There was little known about germs and bacteria, nor about where disease came from. The idea of purifying the sickroom is an old one and in many areas of the country, as well as in Europe, it was still common to burn incense or light sprigs of herbs, to supposedly purify the air. It's closely akin to the idea of driving out evil spirits from a room so as to make the disease go away.

Hygiene was virtually unknown in the area of patient care. There is no doubt that the smells of disease abounded in the sick-room. Floors weren't cleaned as a matter of health prevention, screens or cloths weren't generally used on windows to keep out flies and the idea of fresh air in a room was seen as an entry point for more "bad humors," or evil spirits. Purifying the air was a feeble attempt at dealing with the unknown.

To cure the Flux

Take the inside peeling of leather or scrape it to get the flesh that is sticking on the leather. Place it in some water & boil it very strong then take a tespoon full every half hour & if very bad take a table spoon full until you observe some effect.

The flux was generally recognized as rampant diarrhea or dysentery. Many recipes for treating the flux are based on an astringent, in this case, the soft side of tanned leather. Tannin, which usually was obtained from oak bark, would be the the material that possibly gave some relief. Other astringents often used for this condition include redroot (*Ceanothus americanus*), bayberry powder (*Myrica cerifera*) and persimmon tree bark (*Diospyros virginiana*).

One remedy for the flux that was popular in the South in the mid-1800s, and used often in the War Between the States, was made from boiled, green persimmons. The liquid was added to a bit of alcohol or honey, to help preserve it. When the person would come down with diarrhea, the liquid would be taken throughout the day. Honey was often added simply because the green persimmons had such a puckering taste that it was almost impossible to swallow without the addition of either alcohol or honey.

To Cure Fevers & Ague

Take an ingen turnip & get it & grate it fine..then take it inwardly not much at a time before the chils come on, take it as the (?) if very hard take for of it.

"Ingen turnip" means an Indian turnip, or jack-in-the-pulpit *(Arisaema triphyllum)*. It was a plant commonly used for a variety of things, mainly because the plant's root, if eaten, causes severe, biting pain on the tongue and throat.

Steven Foster, in *The Petersons Field Guide to Medicinal Plants,* said that American Indians made use of the dried root of jack-in-the-pulpit for colds and coughs and as a blood-building agent. It was used as a poultice for treating boils, abscesses and ringworm, as well. There are many historical references of this being used in treating asthma, colds, coughs and bronchitis, in the form of a tea made from the roots. This entry in Slagle's diary reflects the common usage at the time.

A Syrup

Take yellow dock root, burdock root and the root of false bitter sweet of each an equal quantity, pour over enough boiling water to cover them well. Steep for hours without boiling, strain, and sweeten, while hot as sweet syrups, after cooling add one drachm of the Iodide of Potash to the pint. Dose a table spoonfull three times a day.

Yellow dock *(Rumex crispus)* is a plant with a long history of use as a blood purifier, used to treat chronic blood diseases, enlarged lymph glands as well as being used to treat sore throats, diarrhea, skin sores and other ailments.

Burdock root *(Arctium lappa* and *Arctium minus)* was another traditional blood purifier. Usually 2 ounces of the dried root was added to 1 quart of water and boiled, then that liquid administered for stimulating bile secretion, for sweating, used in treating gout, liver and kidney ailments, even rheumatism and gonorrhea. Externally it was used as a wash for eczema and other skin problems. The seeds were used in preparations for treating scarlet fever and smallpox. The fresh leaves, mashed and applied as a poultice, were used on burns, ulcers and other skin sores. American Indians used this plant for centuries before the white races arrived.

False bittersweet is likely to be woody nightshade *(Solanum dulcamara)* which was sometimes called bittersweet on the frontier. It's not a native plant, but had been introduced earlier. The plant was used as an external wash for warts, felons and tumors. Historically it was used as a diuretic, a sweat inducer and for rheumatism, gout, bronchitis, whooping cough. The plant is toxic if misused and can cause vomiting and convulsions. The above syrup recipe would have caused a reaction in the patient, although the woody nightshade could cause complications, even death in some cases. However, since so little was known about disease and medicine in that time, the remedy would likely have not been blamed. Conversely, if the patient recovered, the remedy would certainly be credited.

To Ease All Bad Colds

Take ingen Turnip & dry it & also skink cabbage root & dry it then grate both of them, & take of each one teaspoonfull every night(?) or two.

Indian turnip, or jack-in-the-pulpit *(Arisaema triphyllum)*, shows up in many formulas of the 1800s. It was an intriguing plant because of the biting chemical effect it had on the lips and tongue. Lots of young boys, growing up in rural areas, delighted in having their city friends taste a bit of raw Indian turnip root. The pain is immediate, a combination of tickly and pricking pain that dissipates within five or ten minutes.

"Skink cabbage" is skunk cabbage *(Symplocarpus foetidus)*,

a strongly skunk-scented plant that grows in boggy swamps throughout Georgia, Tennessee and up into New England. The roots were used by American Indians for whooping cough, toothache, cramps and convulsions. The roots were poulticed for wounds and as underarm deodorant. The leaves were used externally in poultice or strong decoction (tea) for treating epilepsy and rheumatism. In large doses the plant is emetic. The roots are considered toxic today, even though they have a long history of usage by people who were familiar with their effects.

In *The Indian Physician, Containing A New System of Practice Founded on Medical Plants,* by Joseph Miller, 1828, there is this entry:

"Skunk Cabbage....It possesses a very acrid pungent quality and may be used for coughs, consumption, fever, asthma, rheumatism, and in all cases where stimulants and expectorants are necessary. One tea spoonful of the powder made of the root, may be taken several times a day, in a gill of hot water."

Dropsy

To cure the first symptoms of the dropsy take the inside bark of elder & iron rust & vinegar. Take say 1 pint of vinegars & 1 small handfull of elder & about the same of iron rust & mix all together & then take one drachm 3 times a day each time before meal times (good days); Keeps down the fever.

Dropsy is an accumulation of diluted lymph in body cavities and tissues. Thomas Palmer, writing in his notebook, *The Admirable Secrets of Physick and Chyrurgery* in the late 1600s, said, "Signs (of dropsy) are swelling of the feet, especially at night, difficult breathing, Palenes (paleness) of the face and eyes, a Cough, sometimes a swelling the legs, great thirst, lost appetite. Retention of stools, of sweat, of Vomiting.....the cause is feebleness of the liver either through heat or cold..."

Elder bark, from a shrub *(Sambucus canadensis)* was used by American Indians as a diuretic, as a laxative and an emetic. It was used poulticed on swollen limbs and cuts. The leaves were poulticed and used on boils, to relieve headaches, to treat a newborn baby's navel, used to stop bleeding on cuts and to treat skin ulcers. A tea made of the inner bark, when combined with peppermint was a folk remedy for colds and nausea and to induce sweating. The leaves, bark and unripe berries contain cyanide and can cause cyanide poisoning if misused in strong doses.

Iron rust would have had little effect other than some coloring and small traces of mineral iron. Vinegar was used as a carrier and to keep the the other ingredients from spoiling or fermenting.

A Sure Remedy for a Felon

Take a pint of common soft soap & stir in air slack lime till it is of the consistency of glazier's putty. Make a leather thimble, fill it with this composition & insert the finger therein & a cure is certain. This is a domestic application that every housekeeper can apply (successfully?).

Felon: A purulent infection at the distal end of a finger near or around the nail or the bone. Such an infection in the days before hydrogen peroxide and first-aid ointments would have been tenacious to cure. The leather thimble, or cone, filed with the soap and lime would keep it soft and covered from air and dirt. The patient had to overcome the injury or illness with his own immune system more than relying upon this remedy to assist.

Slack lime refers to slaked lime and soft soap is made from olive oil rather than animal fat. Soap made with animal fats produced a harder, more solid soap, which would not work in this recipe.

Washing the affected part in soap and water and keeping it covered and away from dirt would have helped more than the above remedy.

A Cure for a Snake Bite

From a private letter from "G.W. K," in Texas, under date of the 27th of April, we copy the following interesting account of his recipe in treating the bite of a rattlesnake, it may furnish a useful hint for further improvisement.

Before I forget it, let me inform you that the medicine chest arrived in due season, and that just as I (opened?) it had made use from (some?) of the articles contained. I was looking over the bottles when one of my men came running in, saying he had been bitten by a rattlesnake. He was holding fast his wrist while two streams of blood were running from one of his fingers, where the fangs of the snake had inserted. As this man does not use tobacco, I told him to fill his mouth with salt and suck as hard as he could at his wounds. I next kept a rag well saturated with hartshorn on the wound to counteract the poison. I then (put?) 20 drops of hartshorn in a teacupful of whiskey and poured it down his throat. In five minutes more I repeated this dish, and in five minutes more I gave him another just like it.

By this time I gave him a full glass of strong whiskey and sixty drops of hartshorn and thought the load was sufficient. The man was an Irishman, and old soldier and took the matter quite cooly. For three quarters of an hour he sat quietly and talked cooly while I kept renewing the hartshorn to the two wounds where the fangs of the snake had bit him. In about an hour he commenced to laughing, then to whistling, next sing, and finally to dance. I had him all right then. I knew that the whiskey had got ahead of the poisons, and had reached his vitals first. In five minutes more he was as drunk as Bacchus, sprawling on the floor, slept half a day, and next morning was at work as well as ever. So much for the first case I ever cured with the contents of the medicine chest. The hartshorn combined with the whiskey effected the thing.

This was obviously copied verbatim from a newspaper account that Slagle had read. He probably thought the account was funny and may have kept it in order to read it again for the entertainment of others.

Heartshorn, or Hart's Horn, is listed in the 1927 *Manual of Materia Medica and Pharmacology, U.S.P. 1820-1830,* as the horn of the stag, a male deer. The hard, bony horns yield by boiling with water a transparent, colorless, inodorous jelly, and then incineration of cleaned bones gives pure calcium phosphate, which was mixed with antimony sulphuret and subjected to white heat, yielding antimony oxide and calcium phosphate. Additional note also indicates that Hart's Horn was a component of the once official antimonial or James' powder. Thus, Hart's Horn was once recognized as an official medical component, and thought to be effective by official pharmaceutical texts and remained listed in those as late as 1927.

What we know now about snakebite is that the ingestion of alcohol is not beneficial to driving out the poisons. However, in the case described above, it sounds as if the doctor gave so much liquids in the form of alcohol that it may have flushed the snake's poisons out of the system. Or, as is more likely the case, the man survived in spite of the doctor's efforts. It's just as possible that the whole story was simply made up to fill up space in the newspaper.

A Liniment For a Bruise
Mix one penny-worth of each of the following, and rub upon the bruise every evening - Spirits of wine, laudanum, camphor, (Opovdeldoe?), (Fat?), Ammnonia and turpentine.

The writing here is so distorted by either moisture on the paper, or by a quill pen that was giving problems, that it is nearly impossible to read entirely. The wine and laudanum (tincture of opium) added to the lard with the turpentine and ammonia would have made a syrupy linament. Laudanum was a common ingredient in many remedies and by its narcotic properties, effective. Many rural physicians, as well as grannywomen and the general population, grew the opium poppy in order to have a supply of opium tincture, or laudanum, for medical purposes.

Turpentine figures prominently in many bruise and skin remedies and was still in use through the 1950s as a purported healing agent. When someone received a bad cut, the injury would be dunked in turpentine or kerosene as the only treatment given.

Tincture Paragoric

Take 1 drachm opium
1 fluidrachm Oil anise
2 ounces honey or shugar
2 scruples camphor
2 pints whiskey

Paregoric was a mixture that every practicing doctor of the 1800s had on hand. It was used as a sedative, both for adults and for babies with the croup, whooping cough and other illnesses. This is a fairly standard home version of that tincture. The anise seed was used as a flavoring, tasting similar to licorice. Honey would have simply sweetened the material, making it more palatable. The camphor gave a jolt to the nose, like smelling salts would, while the whiskey acted as a carrier for the opium.

This was a common medicine, useful for that time, and effective as a sedative due to the opium it contained.

Felon on finger
Take common rock salt such as is used for salting pork or beef; dry it in an oven, then pound it fine mix with spirits of turpentine, in equal parts. Put it in a rag and wrap it around the parts affected, and as it gets dry, put on more; and in twenty four hours we (?) are assured (?) felon will be dead. It will do no harm to try it.

Salt shows up in all kinds of old remedy formulas. Possibly it was because it caused pain, causing the user to feel like some effect was taking place. Turpentine, also, was commonly used for all kinds of ailments and positive benefits were claimed by many people. Kerosene often replaced turpentine in the twentieth century for first-aid uses. The turpentine used in this formula acted as a carrier and minimal binding agent for the salt. If the felon was an open wound, as was often the case, this would have likely been a very painful medicine as both ingredients would cause pain on an open wound.

Sure Cure for Neuralgia
Which is given by a noted physician in Germany who invariably cured the disease which is nothing but a poultice and tea made from our common wild thistle. The leaves are macerated and used on the parts afflicted as a poultice, while a small quantity of the leaves are boiled down to the proportion of a quart to pint and a small wine glass of the decoction drank before each meal.

Note that this remedy is another that sounds as if it has been copied from another source. Advertisements for patent medicines, as well as discussions about illnesses and their remedies were showing up regularly in newspapers by the 1830s. In the 1840s patent medicine sellers started issuing their own almanacs and broadsides to promote their medicines to the public. Many of those almanacs carried descriptions like the one above and the general public would keep the almanacs, pass them around to friends, and often write out the formula to keep handy in their journal or diary. Almanacs combined popular, useful information with lots of advertising.

"Our common thistle" is likely milk thistle (*Silybum marianum*), a European plant that was brought to the U.S. and became naturalized. The young leaves, with the spines removed, was eaten as a greens vegetable. A common appetite stimulant was made from the leaves, stem and flowers, in the form of tea. This plant was also used as a treatment for indigestion, liver problems, for treating jaundice, hepatitis, poisoning from chemicals and many other complaints. Commercial medicines from the seed of this plant are still manufactured in Europe and available in health food stores in the U.S. This remedy in Slagle's book would have had beneficial effects on some ailments although it may not have been effective in treating neuralgia (a paroxysmal pain along a nerve).

Dropsy to Cure

A tea made of chestnut leaves and drank in the place of water will cure most obstinate cases of dropsy in a few days.

Dropsy is a term no longer used today. We know this condition as edema, an accumulation of fluid in the tissues. The word dropsy comes from a Middle English term, dropesie, meaning accumulation of water.

Generally dropsy was treated with a diuretic. Porcher (In *Resources of the Southern Fields and Forests*, 1863) lists chestnut (a tea of the roots or bark) as containing tannin, useful for treating diarrhea for soldiers in the field due to its astringent action.

Scrofulous to cure
A tea made of ripe or dried whortleberries and drank in place of water is a sure and (effective?) cure for a scrofulous difficulty.

Scrofula is listed as a constitutional condition affecting the tissues of the young, characterized by a predisposition to tuberculosis, lymphatism, swellings of the glands and respiratory catarrhs. Scrofulous means anything pertaining to scrofula. A secondary meaning for this word is corrupt or morally degenerate.

Whortleberry is a small European shrub (*Vaccinium myrtillus*) but is listed in Porcher's book as possibly being *Vaccinium arboreum*, an American plant also known as farcle berry. He lists that plant as an astringent, used as a wash in sore mouth and root bark tea used for diarrhea.

Kidney Difficulty
A tea made of peach leaves is a sure cure for this complaint.

Peach leaves, flowers, bark and pits contain cyanide. Porcher lists all of these parts as having been used medicinally for whoopingcough and in stronger doses as a purgative. The use of an astringent would possibly act to stop bleeding of the kidneys if that condition was present. In small doses the amount of cyanide would have not been especially helpful and in larger doses would have caused complications. The patient would "feel" the tea working due to the presence of cyanide, but that did not mean it was in the least way effective.

Cancer to Cure
Plaster made of fresh slacked lime, lard, fresh tar is a sure cure. Which with all its roots (the cancer) will soon come off.

There were lots of skin eruptions that were classified as "cancers." Boils that broke open and were slow to heal, infections, actual skin cancers, were all lumped together under this heading. Many believed that the cancer should not be bandaged and required being open to the air to heal. This lard, tar and lime mixture would draw out some of the drainage of the injury, would seal it up from germs in the air, and would keep the skin somewhat moistened from the lard.

Small Pox to Cure

Apply raw onions halved under the arms in the hands and on the bottom of the feet. Change often. Diet of chicken broth.

Raw onions, garlic and related alliums are still listed as useful medicines as late as the 1916 edition of the *National Standard Dispensatory, Natural History, Chemistry, Pharmacy, Actions and Uses of Medicines*. Onions, both raw and roasted, have been used for centuries for external wounds as well as internal illnesses.

According to Sylvia Windle Humphrey, in *A Matter of Taste*, The Macmillan Co, 1965, p. 161, onions were so important that in 1864 General Ulysses S. Grant said, "I will not move my army without onions." Onions were seen as such an important battlefield wound medicine as well as useful in intestinal problems, that he refused to move his soldiers into battle without a supply. Two days later he reportedly received three train carloads of onions!

In *Letter from a Country Girl* (by Jackson, a widely reprinted story in the Civil War, which prompted posters) girls were advised, "Don't send your sweetheart a love-letter, send him an onion!"

It should be noted, however, that while onions had usefulness in some maladies, the application of raw onions under the arms, in the hands and to the bottoms of the feet, would have done absolutely nothing for smallpox. However, it attests to the lack of any useful remedies for this dread disease. People would try anything, in hope that something might work.

Coughs to Cure
Take 1 pint honey, 2 spoonsfull vinegar, 1 spoonfull alcome jam.

No reference is made to what "alcome jam" may be but is likely to be some type of tart berry jam for flavoring.

Coughing would sometimes respond to such preparations. Something tart, like vinegar and a sour jam, with some honey, would likely have soothed the throat and done no harm.

Janders to Cure
The bark of mulberry root, bark of wild cherry root, of each an equal quantity. Boil strong to one pint, let cool, add one pint rye whiskey.

Janders was common slang for jaundice, which is a yellowing of tissues and bodily fluids with bile, caused by any of several conditions where the body's manufacturing of bile has been interrupted.

Mulberry *(Morus sp.)* is listed as narcotic, sedative, tonic and astringent in *Culbert's Manual of Materia Medica*, 1927. Porcher, in *Resources of the Southern Fields and Forests*, 1863, lists the inner bark, as a powder, for strong purgative and the berries used in syrup as a laxative for children; a tincture of the inner bark of the root was used as a laxative bitter.

The mulberry itself was, and still is, used as an ingredient in pies, syrups, jams and other pleasant foods.

Colory to Cure
1 qt. best brandy 1/2 oz. kain pepper, one sin(...?), 1 oz. cloves, 1 allspice.

Most likely this was one person's spelling for Cholera, (and often pronounced "chol-or-ee") was entered correctly in another formula below. Slagle seemed to carefully preserve the spellings precisely from each of his sources.

Kain pepper was cayenne pepper but the next ingredient is lost to us as the handwriting has faded. The cloves and allspice would simply have been flavoring although may have been seen at the time as medicinal. Sometimes cloves and allspice were looked upon as appetite stimulants in addition to being flavorings.

Cholera to Cure
1 parts laudanum, 1 parts champhorated spirits; 2 parts tincture of ginger; 2 parts capsicum.

Dose - one teaspoonfull in a wine glass of water. If the case is obstinate, repeat the dose in three or four hours.

Cholera is an acute, often fatal infectious, epidemic disease caused by a microorganism. It was characterized by diarrhea, vomiting, cramps and total collapse of the patient.

Laudanum is tincture of opium, a common and readily-available pain killer until the 1900s. Ginger was added for settling the stomach, just as it is often used today. Capsicum is cayenne pepper (listed as "kian" pepper in previous remedy above).

Croup to Cure
A teaspoonfull of pulverized alum in a little molasses is a simple remedy for croup, and one almost always at hand. The dose never fails to give relief; if it should, repeat it after one hour.

The croup was something that children got, a gripping, choking cough, deep in the chest. Alum and molasses would have done little to alleviate this condition, although the alum would tighten the throat a bit and the molasses would have had a mild, soothing effect. Before antibiotics, the patient basically had to be kept as comfortable as possible and wait until the body healed itself.

Felon to Cure

Take a pint of common soft soap and stir it in air-blacked wine until it is of the consistency of glazier's putty. Take a leather thimble, and insert the finger therin. And change the composition once in twenty minutes and a cure is certain.

Felons were a common malady back in these olden times. This illness came about mostly because of lack of sanitary conditions, of infections getting into small injuries of the hands or fingers. Band aids were not in common usage (although were first available near the end of the Civil War, according to Virginia Mescher in *Dates of Selected Inventions and Occurrences During the Latter Part of the 18th Century and During the 19th Century*, 1989). Little was known about keeping a wound clean or covered to prevent infection. Soft soap, as described by a pharmacist is, "A yellowish-green soap made with potash and olive oil." Soft soap was used as a base for many ointments and salves by physicians.

Neuralgia to Cure

Prepare horseradish by grating and mixing in vinegar, the same amounts for table purposes and apply to the temple where the face or head is affected; onto the wrist when the pain is in the arm or shoulder.

Horseradish *(Amoracia rusticana)* was used for poultices, rheumatism and other tendon, joint or muscle complaints due to its properties of irritation of the skin, drawing the blood to the area and causing redness. The strong odor of the horseradish and its activity of opening up the head to breathing was probably also thought to be helpful. Experimentally, horseradish has antitumor activity (according to Foster in *The Peterson Field Guide to Medicinal Plants)*. Horseradish leaves were a common poison to livestock, if eaten in any quantity, therefore most people who grew horseradish, grew it behind a garden fence.

Diphtheria to Cure

Take mullein leaves and steep them in strong vinegar, and put them around the neck and breast as hot as can be borne. Also take a teapot, and put in it one gill of whiskey and one teacupful of vinegar; then have three or four pieces of brick the size of a hen's egg; put them in the fire and make them hot then put one in the kettle at a time, holding the spout in the mouth and swallowing steam. Use one brick every fifteen minutes until relieved. Keep the bowels moderately open; nothing more.

Diphtheria was another of the awful diseases that plagued early settlers on their way West. The whiskey and vinegar steam would have given a bit of temporary relief to the lungs and head, but little else and would not affect a cure.

Frozen Feet

Turpentine & camphor gum mix.

If you lived in the mid-1800s, on your homestead and you got severe frostbite, it could be a life or death matter. Untreated, your frozen limbs might wither away, causing infection and disease. Footwear and clothing wasn't as sophisticated as it is today.

Gloves were mostly hand-made, from home-tanned animal skins. There was little insulation in boots or socks. If you worked outdoors, as everyone on a farmstead had to, you ran the risk of frozen toes and fingers. Frostbite was very common, as attested to by the many useless formulas for treating it.

Salt Kherim (?)
Take tincture of myrrh, and while drying the hands pour some on the hand and rub it in well. It is well to take something to purify the blood, whild cherry bark in whiskey is good.

The word, "Kherim" isn't clear as to its meaning. Myrrh has been used for centuries and still shows up in late twentieth century formulas for hand ointments. This one from a pharmacist: 1 oz. comfrey, 1 Tbsp. goldenseal, 1 Tbsp. ground or powdered myrrh in a mixture of equal parts coconut and mineral oils and vaseline. Myrrh is a resin from wood, and like other wood resins, had a healing, styptic effect.

Chilblains is an inflammation followed by itchy irritation on the hands, feet, or ears, resulting from exposure to moist cold. In other words, another result of exposure to cold or frostbite. Like recipes for treating frostbite, there are numerous ones for chilblains, as seen in the following two.

Chilblains
On retiring at night, rub the parts fast of the foot with sperm oil and hold the foot out near a good hot stove or grate until the heat (ceases?) to burn then remove it to cool a little. Then heat it again, and repeat do so three or four times every night for four or five nights, and I will insure a perfect cure.

Chilblains

Take two good size cabage stumps, pare off the hard outer (skin?), then the pith or inside and slice very thin. Put into a spider with one teacup of good sweet lard and cook slowly till there is nothing left but a soft mess of the cabbage. Strain off the lard, and after soaking the feet and wiping them dry, grease them thoroughly with this lard, and heat in by the fire. Grease them every night and heat them as hot as can be borne and my word for it, a cure will come.

Note: A "spider" as listed here is a cast iron frying pan with a long handle.

Diphtheria

A few drops of sulphuric acid in a tumblerful of water. The result of this mixture is said to be a coagulation of the diphtheritic membrane and its ready removal by coughing.

Sulfuric acid is a highly corrosive, dense, oily liquid, colorless to brown depending upon its purity. It is used in the manufacture of a wide variety of chemicals including fertilizers, paints and detergents. It has a suffocating sulfurous odor, sometimes used as a bleaching agent and disinfectant. Diphtheria was so frightening that even mixtures as useless and dangerous as this were used.

When the voice is lost

As some times the case, from the effects of a cold, a simple pleasant remedy is furnished by beating up the white of one egg, adding to it the juice of one lemon and sweetening with white sugar to taste. Take a teaspoonfull from time to time. It has been known to effectually cure the ailment.

Consumption
Remedy - whole mustard seed, Dose - one tablespoon-ful each morning before breakfast.

Consumption, an early name for tuberculosis, was contagious and when it broke out in a community, was as frightening as any disease could be. It affected the lungs, or sometimes settled in the bones and other parts of the body. Once contracted, the patient would slowly waste away, or be "consumed" by the disease. People would try anything, even something as useless as the whole mustard seed here.

Mustard seed has been used for many ailments, especially as a heating agent in mustard plasters.

Chilblains
Soak the feet in strong potato water, those potatoes have been boiled until they are soft. Leave the potatoes in. Use as hot as can be borne one or two applications is generally sufficient.

Potato water is mostly starch and not effective in treating this malady, especially if applied hot to already numb flesh.

Cure for Piles (bleeding piles)
(Wild?) carot weed usually known amongst farmers, I believe as ragweed. (Pick?) leaves until the blossoms appear, then use them always in preference. I used to wilt the leaves by holding them before the fire, or leaving them on a warm stove; (?) (Also?) use them in decoction, and bathing with it, being careful to have it very strong. (But?) use always your own (judgement?) so that you give it a fair trail. Always use the weed instead of paper, Continue its use until the plant disappears in the fall. Keep your feet dry and your self out of the wet as much as possible; but after

a cure has been effected. I have never known to return through exposure.

Being wet and suffering from exposure was the attributed cause for lots of maladies. People were encouraged to bathe infrequently, believing that being wet encouraged all kinds of illness. Ragweed *(Abrosia artemisiafolia* and *A. trifida)* shows up in many remedies for hemorrhoids, often in the form of a salve or ointment. This is a simpler, and likely less effective method of using the plant's wilted leaves instead of toilet tissue.

"Use in place of paper" refers to the fact that toilet tissue was not generally available. It was common to save newspapers and catalogs for this purpose and the practice continued well into the 1950s in many rural areas. The use of the abrasive paper would often cause irritations.

Ragweed is highly astringent, emetic and used for fevers, nausea, minor skin eruptions and on insect bites. Made into a salve or ointment, it would have likely been helpful with hemorrhoids.

Rheumatism

1 pint(?) of 90 per cent alcohol, 1 oz. gum myrrh, 1 oz. cayenne pepper, 1 oz. gum camphor, 2 drachms cinnamon oil, 2 drachms oil of cloves; let it stand a few days before using. Bathe the part affected, then cover with a cloth, drink with cold water. The flesh will (object?), but a few applications will (?) it is also good for pain in the stomach and bowels.

Rheumatism covers all kinds of pathological conditions of the muscles, tendons, joints and bones or nerves characterized by pain and discomfort. Rheumatoid arthritis, a chronic disease that is characterized by inflammation of joints, stiffness, weakness and loss of motion, still is a persistent problem in today's world, particularly in older people. Newer treatments exist, mostly meant to reduce inflammation and ease the pain, but little actual progress has been made in controlling this malady since this remedy was recorded.

Myrrh, cayenne pepper, camphor gum and cinnamon and cloves would have made a somewhat pleasant medicine. The plant parts would have acted primarily to bring blood to the affected area in the same way that products containing capsicin (cayenne pepper oil) are used today. Heet, Ben Gay and others in that category, are simply newer versions of this old formula!

Ague or Chills and Fever

Take a piece of muslin or any thin goods (cloth) and cut it so it will cover the back from neck to hips, and (cover?) to the back; then take common cotton batting and tack (sew) it on so it will be about an inch in thickness, (Secure?) it on to the necked back and wear it there for 2 or 3 months and you will have no more ague. Never know it to fail.

Note the length of the cure, "(put) it on to the necked back and wear it there for 2 or 3 months..." In that length of time, the illness should have abated from natural means.

This entry is also telling about other parts of life in the mid-1800s. The mere fact that cotton batting would have been worn next to the skin for 2 or 3 months, tells us a great deal about people's clothing. Certainly tidy people would have washed this material from time to time, but those away from civilization might not. The washing of clothes was a hard chore, requiring a tub, scrub board and lye soap. Clothes were generally boiled in a kettle first, then scrubbed on the washboard with soap, then rinsed. Clothes were also beaten with wooden paddles if a washboard wasn't at hand. Many people from this era believed strongly that it was the washing of clothes that wore them out, rather than the accumulation of dirt and grime, and they would go for weeks, even months, before washing their clothes. Old-timers from that time described putting on their long johns on September first and not taking them off until the first of May. This remedy also speaks to the fact that people believed that frequent bathing caused illness.

Chills and Fever

Of 20 grams of blue mass, 20 grains quinine, 20 drops of oil black pepper. Make into 16 pills. Take one every hour between the chills and fever, or fever and chills until you have taken from 4 to 6; then if the chills return, when the fever subsides proceed in the same manner; when chills stop get about 10 cents worth of yellow pacoon root, put it in one pint of good whiskey and take a little several times every day for several days. Good.

Ten cents worth of yellow pacoon is most likely Puccoon, (*Lithospermum canescens*). It flowers orange to yellow, April through June. American Indians are recorded as having used tea from the leaf as a wash for fevers when accompanied by spasms. The tea-wash was also used by people who had been near someone with convulsions.

Porcher, in *Resources of the Southern Fields and Forests*, 1863, lists Puccoon as *Sanguinaria canadensis* or bloodroot. The designation of "yellow pacoon" above distinguishes it from bloodroot.

Chillblains and Neuralgia

Take one ounce each of Chloroform, hartshorn, turpentine, oil of spike and sweet oil; shake well, and apply three or four times a day; heat in by the fire. Good.

Chilblain is an inflammation that is followed by itching and irritation on feet, hands and ears that is a result of exposure to moist cold. Neuralgia is a recurrent intensification of pain in a nerve. Exposure to the elements during winter while-going about the normal work of the farm often resulted in these conditions. The itching and pain could be intense and returned at the slightest re-exposure to cold.

Harts horn, made from stag's horn, was a common medication and generally available, as was turpentine (which comes from pine). Spike oil is listed in most Pharmacopeas as coming from *Lavendula spicata*, or the common lavender plant. Oil of lavender was considered best from the British *Lavandula vera*, which produced a more fragrant oil. Spike oil was common and generally available in the mid-1800s in general stores as well as being a common ingredient in rural doctor's bags.

Croup
A piece of lard as big as a butternut rubbed up with sugar. Divide into 3 parts and give at intervils of 20 minutes.

The lard would have lubricated the throat. Mixing lard with sugar would not be too different than getting a child to eat raw cookie dough and this probably was a somewhat pleasant but ineffective remedy.

Frosted Limbs
It is anounced are permanent believed by one or two applicatons of a boiled lye of wood ashes, make as strong as to be quite slippery between the fingers. This lye should settle, be drained off, with (siphon?) a large handfull of common salt to each quart of lye mixed with it. It should be quite warm and the limbs be submerged for one or two hours.

Nothing was known about nerve injury and the assumption was the best way to treat frostbite was to warm up the injured flesh as hot as could be stood. This treatment would have likely done more harm than good. Lye, when added to water, causes it to heat up. Most people, including my own family, continued making their own lye from wood ashes well into the 1900s. The process was to dump wood ashes from the stove into a hopper or wooden funnel, then slowly pour water through the ashes, catching it in a pail. That water would be left alone for a few hours so that the lye could settle to the bottom, then the clearer water on top would be siphoned off and discarded. The remaining material in the bottom of the bucket would be allowed to evaporate, then the dried lye would be collected for use in making soap or for soaking the hulls from hominy corn and for other uses.

Diphtheria
Four drops of carbolic acid in a half a wine glass of water, is said to be an infallible remedy for diphtheria.

Diphtheria is another of the serious illnesses that have been fairly well controlled today. In Mr. Slagle's time, diphtheria was serious, often deadly. It was an infectious disease that caused difficulty in breathing, accompanied by high fever and weakness. It was often harmful to the tissues of the heart and central nervous system and resulted in prolonged ill health and a weakened condition throughout the rest of the patient's life.

Carbolic acid is listed as phenol, "caustic, poisonous," in the dictionary. This demonstrates how desperate people were to find remedies for diphtheria.

Small Pox Remedy. Good.
It is harmless when taken by well persons. It will also cure scarlet fevers.

Sulphate of zinc (?). Fox glove (digitalis), 1 grain; a teaspoonfull of sugar; mix, with two tablespoons of water, then thoroughly mixed, adding 4 ounces of water. Take a

glass full every hour. Either disease will disappear in twelve hours. For a child smaller glasses according to age.

The preface that this remedy is harmless when taken by well persons demonstrates the fear people had of disease. Often people would take a remedy when they were well, hoping that it might keep them from coming down with the illness. Some of the old remedies were caustic and by this notation of "harmless when taken by well persons" gives the fearful person leave to go ahead and take this in the event it might possibly help them avoid smallpox.

The active ingredient, digitalis, was not a plant to be experimented with. It was, and still is, used as a heart stimulant, but using the wrong amount could cause death.

Hydrophobia

Elecampane 2 ounces, to be boiled in a pint of new milk and taken in the morning after the patient has fasted all night. That he is to continue fasting six hours after taking it, and that the dose is to be repeated 3 times on three successive mornings, as soon as possible after the person has been bitten. Elcampane Root can be taken on 3 alternative days. (Fast?) past the 6 hours after each dose.

Hydrophobia, or rabies, was a fearful disease and remains so today. It is commonly passed on through the saliva of a rabid animal through a break in the skin, such as through a bite. Mad dogs were much feared and there were many so-called treatments for the disease once it developed. Mad stones, special porous stones believed to have power to pull out the poison from a mad dog's bite were valued implements in many communities and would be passed down from one generation to the next. Nearly every community had someone who possessed a mad stone, which would be borrowed and used if someone was bitten by a suspected rabid animal. Lots of purported remedies existed but true cures were not available.

Elecampane *(Inula helenium)* is not an indigenous plant to the U.S., but had been introduced and spread throughout many states. It is commonly found today along roadsides, fencerows and fields. Tea, made of the root, was a common folk remedy for pneumonia, coughs, asthma, upset stomach and other complaints. In current studies it has been shown to have sedative effects on experimental animals.

Croup
Take the white of an egg, (broken) in sweetened water is a sure cure for the croup, the remedy to be repeated till a cure is affected.

The croup is a condition affecting the larynx in children. It is accompanied by breathing difficulty and a harsh cough. Lots of remedies existed in folk medicine simply because it was frustrating to see a child cough so hard and parents would try anything that seemed to help. Although the above certainly wasn't a cure, like most of the folk remedies that were passed around for croup, it did soothe the throat briefly. Cough syrups of the next century did little more than this old mixture and were often nothing more than heavy sugar water, glycerine, coloring and something added for flavoring.

Sure Cure for Smallpox.
By the use of cream of tartar, take an ounce of cream of tartar dissolved in a pint of water and drink at intervals after cooling is a certain, never failing remedy. It has cured thousands never leaves a (?), never causes blindness.

Smallpox, which has been essentially wiped out of our culture today, was once a dreaded disease. It is highly infectious, caused by a virus (which doctors didn't know about in 1859) and characterized by chills, high fever, backache and with subsequent eruption of pimples that eventually blister, produce pus and form pockmarks. Lots of "sure-cure" remedies were passed around, all intended to alleviate fear as well as the disease. The doctor (if that is where this remedy originated) likely was trying to assure someone that smallpox could be subdued with this remedy. After all, people didn't want "pretty good" or "sometimes helpful" remedies, but rather listed their home cures always as "sure cure" remedies. Someone may have taken the above cream of tartar water just at the time their fever broke from the natural course of smallpox, and the remedy was attributed with curing the condition.

Little was known of how smallpox spread from person to person, neither what caused it nor what should be done about it once it was contracted.

Elias Slagle, taken at Pittsburg, Kansas, October 10, 1891, age 58
Photo courtesy of Bushwhacker Museum, Nevada, Missouri.

References

A Matter of Taste, Sylvia Windle Humphrey, 1965, Macmillan Press.

American Indian Medicine, Virgil Vogel, 1970, Univ. of Oklahoma Press

Civil War Plants & Herbs, Patricia Mitchell, 2001.

Dates of Selected Inventions and Occurrences During the Latter Part of the 18th Century and During the 19th Century, Virginia Mescher, 1990, Nature's Finest, P.O. Box 10211, Burke, VA 22009.

Flora of Missouri, Julian Steyermark; Iowa State Univ. Press, 1963.

From Blackberries to Fishing Worms; Glimpses of Herbal Medicine Toward the End of the Nineteenth Century, Willie Jordan Batts, 1880; Country Doctor Museum, Bailey, NC, 1987.

Herbal Medicines of the Santa Fe Trail, Jim Long, 1996, Long Creek Herbs publisher.

Hortus Third, Staff of Bailey Horotorium, Cornell Univ.; McMillan Pub., 1976.

Materia Medica and Pharmacology (Comprising the Organic and Inorganic Drugs Which are or Have Been Recognized by the United States Pharmacopeia and National Formulary), David Culbreth, Ph.G., M.D.; Lea & Febiger, 1927.

National Standard Dispensatory, Hobart Hare, B.Sc, M.D.; Lea & Febiger, 1916.

Native American Ethnobotany, Daniel Moerman, 2001, Timber Press.

Patent Medicines in North Carolina, Country Doctor Museum, Bailey, NC, 1994.

Peterson Field Guide to the Medicinal Plants of the Eastern & Central U.S., Steven Foster/James Duke; Houghton Mifflin, 1990.

Resources of the Southern Fields & Forests, Francis Porcher, 1863; Arno & NY Times Press, 1970.

Stamps, Jerry, P.D. private collection medical formulas & plant references.

Squire's Companion to the British Pharmacaopeia, 1896.

The Indian Physician Containing A New System of Practice Founded on Medical Plants, Joseph Miller, 1828.

The Admirable Secrets of Physick & Chyrurgery, Thomas Palmer cir. 1690; republished by Yale University, 1984.

Young's Great Book of Secrets, F.E. Phelan, Montreal, circ. 1872..

Index

Destemper on Doggs

take Sulphure & Cappous an
equal quantity of each, pulverise
bothe, & then stir them in Sweete
Milk, to desolve, & to giv this to
the dogg, you giv him some Milk
thwith out anny thing in it,
then pore but little of this
mixture in the milk you giv
him at different times of the
day say twice, you will take
a heaping teaspoon full of
Sulpher & the same of Cappous
pulverised to one half pint
swette Milk.

A Cleansing & Healing Salve

Take inside Bark of Boartree, Shomak,
root & Bitter sweet root of the 2
formes an equal quantity of the
latter as much as the two together,
fry them in hogs Lard or fat,
Put by for use.

Bittersweet root Salve.
A good hand full of the bark
of the root & 3/4 of a pint of hogs lard.

Bite of a Snake
Take a table spoon full of Olive
Oil inwardly & anoint the wound
well with it.

A most certain Remedy for a pain
Take Oba———— & rub the part
affected.

The following books also by Jim Long are available from
Long Creek Herbs, P.O. Box 127, Blue Eye, MO 65611
For a complete catalog, write, or go to Jim's website:
www.Longcreekherbs.com
(More titles available than are listed here)

Herbal Medicines on the Santa Fe Trail

The Santa Fe Trail was an historic trade route that brought
cayenne peppers up the Trail to St. Louis and Kansas City
and sent back diseases the indigenous people had never
seen. Rugged people traveled the Trail, taking along new
state-of-the-art (for the time) medicines, as well as discover-
ing new plants along the way. This is a look at the plants and
medicines that shaped the medical treatments of the Civil
War and helped to shape our medicines of today.

Herbal Medicines on the Santa Fe Trail **4.95** *(plus $2 postage)*

Recipes & Cooking Practices of the Civil War

Historical recipes and cooking information from the time of
the Civil War from notable historical figures and soldiers.
Includes some folk remedies and a brief history of several
recipes, too.

Recipes & Cooking Practices of the Civil War **4.95**
(plus $2 postage)

Classic Herb Blends

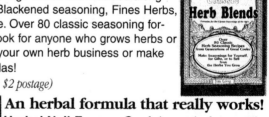

Ever need the formula for Curry Powder or wonder exactly
what goes in Mexican seasoning? Those are included along
with the formulas for Cajun Blackened seasoning, Fines Herbs,
Bouquet Garni and lots more. Over 80 classic seasoning formulas in all. A very useful book for anyone who grows herbs or
cooks. You could even start your own herb business or make
lots of gifts with these formulas!

Classic Herb Blends **4.95** *(plus $2 postage)*

An herbal formula that really works!

Herbal Nail Fungus Soak is made from anti-
fungal herbs that work on many kinds of nail
fungus, as well as athlete's foot and other fungal problems. It's easy to use – you simply
soak for a couple of minutes morning and night.
One box is enough for daily soaks for several weeks, with some left
over. Complete directions for making and using the Soak included. It's
easy to use, and it works! Guaranteed.

Herbal Nail Fungus Soak - $9.95 *(plus $2 postage)*